Paddington's
Opposites
by Michael Bond

Illustrated by John Lobban
Devised by Carol Watson

Viking

Text copyright © Michael Bond, 1990
Illustrations copyright © William Collins Sons &
Co. Ltd., 1990
All rights reserved.
First Published in 1990 by William Collins Sons & Co. Ltd.
First American edition published 1991 by
Viking, a division of Penguin Books USA, Inc.
375 Hudson Street New York, NY 10014
Manufactured in U.S.A.

on

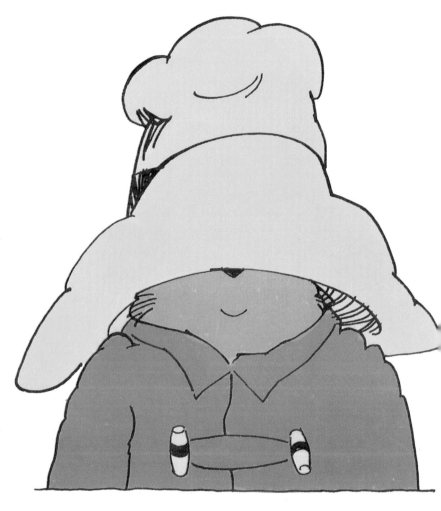

big

small

up

down

in

out

hot

cold

front

back

neat

messy

awake

asleep

wet

dry

open

closed

happy

sad

full

empty

clean

dirty

many

few

straight

crooked

Match the opposites.